G. Schirmer's Collection of Operas

GOUNOD

ROMEO

AND

JULIET

G. SCHIRMER, INC., NEW YORK

G. SCHIRMER'S COLLECTION OF OPERAS.

(ROMEO AND JULIET)²

Opera in Five Acts

BY

CHARLES (GOUNOD)

WORDS BY

J. BARBIER AND M. CARRÉ

THE ENGLISH VERSION BY

DR. THEO. BAKER

WITH AN ESSAY ON THE HISTORY OF THE OPERA BY

W. J. HENDERSON

G. SCHIRMER ~ NEW YORK

ROMEO AND JULIET.

FIRST PERFORMED AT THE THÉÂTRE LYRIQUE, PARIS, APRIL 27, 1867.

Characters of the Drama,

With the Original Cast as presented at the first Performance.

JULIET	Soprano	Mme. CARVALHO
STEPHANO	Soprano	Mme. DARAM
GERTRUDE	Mezzo-soprano	Mme. DUCLOS
ROMEO	Tenor	M. MICHOT
TYBALT	Tenor	M. PUGET
BENVOLIO	Tenor	M. LAURENT
MERCUTIO	Baritone	M. BARRÉ
PARIS	Baritone	M. LAVEISSIÈRE
GREGORIO	Baritone	M. TROY (jeune)
CAPULET	Basso cantante	M. TROY
FRIAR LAURENCE	Bass	M. CAZAUX
THE DUKE	Bass	M. CHRISTOPHE

Guests of the Capulets; Relatives and Retainers of
the Capulets and Montagues.

SCENE, VERONA.

ACT I.—CAPULET'S PALACE. ACT II.—THE GARDEN OF JULIET. ACT III.—THE CELL OF FRIAR LAURENCE; THEN A PUBLIC SQUARE BEFORE CAPULET'S PALACE. ACT IV.—JULIET'S CHAMBER. ACT V.—TOMB OF THE CAPULETS.

" Romeo and Juliet."

Charles Gounod was born in Paris, June 17, 1818, and died in that city, October 18, 1893. His "Roméo et Juliette" occupies the second position of merit on the brief list of his operas, the first place, of course, being awarded to "Faust". The excellence of the libretto of the latter opera naturally led Gounod to go to its makers, when he conceived the desire to write a lyric work on the familiar love-tragedy of Shakespeare. That he should have entertained such an idea was almost inevitable, for he must have felt that the situations of the story offered abundant opportunities for the composition of pure lyric music, in which he excelled. The tragedy of

"Romeo and Juliet" had tempted many opera-composers before Gounod. Among them may be mentioned Dalayrac, Steibelt, Zingarelli, Vaccai, Bellini, and Marchetti, while Hector Berlioz had made it the subject of a dramatic symphony. The librettists of "Faust", Jules Barbier and Michael Carré, arranged the book, which some dramatic critics have praised as being an admirable adaptation of Shakespeare's play. Mlle. de Bovet, a French biographer of Gounod, has very sensibly said, however, that "all Jules Barbier's cleverness could not make the plot other than a love-duet, or rather a succession of love-duets".

While this is true, it is also a fact that the libretto presents the salient incidents of Shakespeare's tragedy in a compact and well-connected manner. In the endeavor to increase the number of parts for young women singers, the librettists introduced Stephano, the page, a character not found in the original play, and having no necessary connection with the story.

They may be forgiven this concession to the demands of operatic tradition, for the sake of the other excellences of their work. Gounod's music has been censured for its monotony, and the critics have generally agreed that this is due to the continual love-duet. A more pointed criticism is that which notes the similarity in the general style of these love-passages to those in "Faust". This similarity cannot well be questioned, and it forces comparisons which are not favorable to the music of "Romeo and Juliet". The love-scenes in "Faust" are the products of genuine inspiration, and they rise to a level of real greatness, seldom attained by the music of "Romeo and Juliet".

In regard to this aspect of the work, M. Arthur Pougin has well said: "If one wished to enter into what might be called a psychological analysis of the score, it would be necessary to discover how great were the difficulties of the composer in writing 'Romeo' without repeating himself, after having written 'Faust'. For, although the subjects of the two works differ widely, we see the same situations reproduced in each, under the same scenic conditions, and the stumbling-block was all the more troublesome, since these situations were the most salient ones, and constituted, as it were, the very core of the dramatic action. Witness the balcony-scene of 'Romeo' and the garden-scene of 'Faust', or the duel of Romeo and Tybalt, with the death of the latter in the first, and the duel of Faust and Valentine, also mortal, in the second. Truly, a musician must have a singular power, a very remarkable faculty of reiteration, to attempt, successfully, such a repetition of similar episodes".

Gounod was not the only man of high ability who attempted to do a second time what he had done at first to perfection. His failure to equal his first performance is certainly a demonstration of the limited power of his imagination; but, outside of the ranks of geniuses of the first order, such as Shakespeare and Goethe, no one has produced a second work so similar in character to a first, and yet so crowded with new beauties, as Gounod did in his "Romeo and Juliet". It is, beyond dispute, an opera of genuine and notable beauty. In the hands of artists, this work never fails to touch the heart of public enthusiasm; and in America, it has certainly grown greatly in favor since, in recent years, it has been performed by a company of singers of the first rank.

It would be uncomplimentary to the reader to tell the familiar story of "Romeo and Juliet", but it is necessary to outline it as it is given in the libretto of Barbier and Carré. The prelude contains a scene in which all the characters are grouped on the stage, and reference is made to the unhappy feud between the houses of Montague and Capulet. The first act takes place in the home of the Capulets. A ball is in progress in honor of Juliet's début in society. Juliet is formally introduced by her father, and subsequently expresses her happiness in the vocal waltz. To the ball, as maskers, come Romeo, Mercutio, and some of their friends. The first meeting of Romeo and Juliet takes place, and love at first sight follows. The appearance of Tybalt, who recognizes Romeo, gives rise to some dialogue, revealing to the lovers the identity of their respective families. Romeo and his friends leave the ball.

In the second act, we have the familiar balcony-scene of the Shakespearean drama. The interview of the lovers is briefly interrupted by the passage of the watch, whose suspicions of the presence of a stranger in the grounds are put to rest by the nurse. The love-scene then continues till the fall of the curtain. In the following scene, Romeo and Juliet go to the cell of Friar Laurence, and are married. In the third act, the feud between the two houses breaks out. Stephano, Romeo's page, fights with Tybalt, and Mercutio also fights with him, and is slain. Tybalt tries to force a quarrel with Romeo, but he declines the combat, until he is impelled to take vengeance for the death of Mercutio, his kinsman. Then he kills Tybalt, and is instantly overcome with horror and remorse, because Tybalt is Juliet's cousin. The Duke arrives upon the scene, and Capulet lays his complaint before him. The Duke sentences Romeo to exile, but the young man declares that he prefers death.

The rising of the curtain on the fourth act discovers Romeo and Juliet together in Juliet's chamber. Their love-scene is ended by the breaking of day, and Romeo is compelled to depart. Capulet enters and informs his daughter that he has chosen for her a husband, the Count Paris. In despair, she asks the aid of the Friar, who is present. He gives her a phial containing a drug to put her in a condition closely resembling death. The final scene shows us Juliet in her tomb. Romeo, returning to seek her, finds her, as he believes, dead. He slays himself, but before he breathes his last, Juliet revives, and the lovers join in one final outburst of despairing love before both die. It will be seen from this outline that the librettists succeeded in preserving the entire tragic action of the original play, while omitting the lighter scenes, such as those of Juliet with her mother and the nurse.

It is not necessary to enter into a detailed consideration of the music, which is very well able to speak for itself. In the first act, the most melodious and pleasing numbers are the solo of Capulet, the song of Mercutio describing Queen Mab, Juliet's waltz-song, and the first duet of the lovers. The waltz-song is a mere exhibition-aria, altogether out of place, and inserted only out of deference to a long-established custom. The second act consists almost wholly of the balcony-scene, and here Gounod's ability as a lyric writer is delightfully displayed. The music is, perhaps, a little too sentimental and not sufficiently passionate, but it is melodious and poetic. In the next scene, there is nothing remarkable, though the passage sung after the wedding usually pleases the hearers.

The following scene, in which Mercutio and Tybalt are killed, leans somewhat toward the style of Meyerbeer, but it lacks the theatrical vigor of that composer. On the other hand, the declamatory air of the tenor at its close is one of Gounod's most effective passages. In the fourth act, the composer is indeed at home, and here we meet with the most satisfying music of the opera. The duet, "Non, ce n'est pas le jour", is a finely dramatic piece of composition, and ranks with the best products of its writer's imagination. In the remainder of the opera, the only things to which especial attention need be called, are the charming orchestral accompaniment to Friar Laurence's announcement of his plan to save Juliet—heard again when she sleeps in the tomb—and the final love-duet.

"Roméo et Juliette" was produced at the Théâtre Lyrique, Paris, April 27, 1867, with Mme. Miolan-Carvalho as Juliet, and M. Michot as Romeo. The rôle of Juliet has been one of Mme. Adelina Patti's favorites, but the best cast of "Romeo and Juliet" in recent times, and probably the best ever brought together, was that of the Metropolitan Opera House at the opening of the season of 1894–95. It consisted of Mme. Melba as Juliet, Mlle. de Vigne as Stephano, Mlle. Bauermeister as the Nurse, M. Jean de Reszké as Romeo, M. Edouard de Reszké as Friar Laurence, M. Plançon as Capulet, Signor Gromzeski as Mercutio, M. Castelmary as the Duke, and M. Mauguiere as Tybalt.

W. J. HENDERSON.

Index.

1

Romeo and Juliet.

Overture-Prologue

with Chorus.

CHARLES GOUNOD.

1

4

*) This Chorus is to be sung by all the artists who interpret the *soli* of this score.

6

(Curtain.)

naî - tre leurs a - mours!_
a - ges could re - move!_

naî - tre leurs a - mours!_
a - ges could re - move!_

naî - tre leurs a - mours!_
a - ges could re - move!_

Standing arm in Father's

Act I.

Nᵒ 1. The Capulets' Ball.

Introduction.

Et com-pli-ce Le cœur glis-se Au ca-
Sli-ly steal-ing, Soft com-pel-ling, All too

pri-ce Du ha-sard!
will-ing Hearts in-vade!

13

13203

Allegretto. (♩=92) **Tybalt.**

Eh! bien? cher Pâ-ris!_____ que vous sem-ble
How now, my dear Pa - ris! Art thou gaz-ing

Paris.

De la fê-te des Ca-pu-lets?_____ Ri - chesse et beauté tout en -
On our fest-al and fair ar - ray?_____ What rich - es and beau-ty a -

sem - ble Sont les hô - tes de ce pa - lais!__
maz - ing Are with - in this pal - ace to - day!__

Tybalt.

Vous n'en voy - ez pas la mer - veil - le, Le tré - sor u - nique et sans
But as yet no note hast thou tak - en Of the rar - est trea - sure we

Paris.

prix, Qu'on des - tine à l'heureux Pâ - ris.__ Si mon cœur en -
own, That is__ des - tin'd for thee a - lone!__ If naught yet my

co - re som - meil - le, Le moment est proche où l'a - mour Viendra l'éveil - ler à son
heart could a - wak - en, Now the time is near that shall move It to a - wak - en un - to

Tybalt.

tour.__ Il s'é - veil - le - ra,__ il s'é - veil - le - ra, je l'es - pè -
love!__ It shall yet a - wake,__ it shall yet a - wake, or I won -

24

13203

26

28

grâ - ce Fait l'a - veu tout bas! Qui reste à sa place Et ne dan - se
corn Up - on her toe, I vow! An - y la - dy here Who is dain - ty

pas, De quel - que dis - grâ - ce Fait l'a - veu tout bas! Ô re - gret ex -
now, She doth wear a corn Up - on her toe, I vow! By'r La - dy! My

trê - me! Quand j'é - tais moins vieux, Je gui - dais moi - mê - me Vos é - bats jo -
day for a mea - sure is gone, Tho' gal - lant more gay nev - er vis - or put

yeux! Les dou - ces pa - ro - les Ne me coûtaient rien! Que
on! To la - dy's ear oft I a love - tale would tell, And

d'a - veux fri - vo - les Dont je me sou - viens!
whis - per - ing soft, I could please her right well!

13203

32

place_____ aux_____ dan - seurs!
way_____ for_____ the ball!

place_____ aux_____ dan - seurs!
way_____ for_____ the ball!

13203

№ 1 bis. Scene.

si les Ca - pu-lets sont gens à se fà - cher, C'est lâ - che - té de nous ca -
If they think we came to quar - rel or de - ride, We should be cow'rds were we to

Tempo moderato. *ben ritmato.*

cher, Car nous a-vons tous là de quoi leur te-nir tê - te!
hide; For ev-'ry man of us has where-with-al to curb them!

Oui, nous a-vons tous là de quoi leur te-nir tê - te! ___
Ay, ev-'ry man of us has where-withal to curb them! ___

6 TENORS.

Oui, nous a-vons tous là de quoi leur te-nir tê - te! ___
Ay, ev-'ry man of us has where-withal to curb them! ___

6 BASSES.

Oui, nous a-vons tous là de quoi leur te-nir tê - te! ___
Ay, ev-'ry man of us has where-withal to curb them! ___

Nº 2. Ballade of Queen Mab.

nais, sub-ti - le den - telle, Ont e - té dé-cou - pés dans l'ai -
top a grass-hop-per's wing, And a this-tle-down spring! Her driv -

pp

le. De quel - que ver - te sau - te - rel - le Par son co -
er, A small grey gnat, he made the cov - er, That she may

cher, le mou-che - ron! Un os de gril-lon sert de
lie well in the shade. A film is the lash of her

manche À son fouet, ___ dont la mè - che blanche Est
whip, And the stock, ___ is a crick-et - bone; 'Twas

prise au ra - yon qui s'é - panche De Phœ-bé ras-sem - blant ___ sa
wound from the rays of the moon When high it shone in the sky ___ a-

vare en son gî - te som - bre, Elle ou - vre des tré - sors____ sans
mi - ser, in sor - did slum - ber, Sees rich - es more than he____ can

nom - bre, Et la li - ber - té rit dans l'ombre Au pris - on -
num - ber, And the pris - on - cell chill and som - bre, Brightens in

nier char - gé de fers.____ Le sol - dat rê - ve d'embus-
free - dom's ray sub - lime!____ And the sol - dier dreams of am - bus-

pp

ca - des, De ba - tail - les et d'es - to - ca -
cades,____ Of healths five fath - om deep, and Span - ish blades,____

poco ritardando.

des, El - le lui ver - se les ra - sa - des
____ Wak - en'd by roar - ing can - non - ades____ He

poco ritardando.

41

Nº 2 bis. Recit. and Scene.

46

13203

Ce jour en — — cor! Dou —
Yet one day more! Like

ce flam — — me, Je te
a trea — — sure I will

gar — — de dans mon à — —
guard thee, naught my plea — —

me Com — — me un tré — sor! Je
sure E'er will re — store! In

veux vi — — vre Dans ce rè —
my fai — ry Dream I'd rev —

ve____ qui m'en - i - vre____
el,____ gay and air - y,____

Ce__ jour en - cor! Dou -
Yet__ one day__ more! Like

ce flam - me,____ Je te
a trea - sure____ I will

gar - de____ dans mon à -
guard____ thee,____ naught my plea -

me____ sure____ Com - - - -me un tré - sor!
sure____ E'er - - - - will re - store!

veux vi - vre___ Dans ce rê - -
my fai - ry___ Dream I'd rev - -

ve___ qui m'en - i - vre___ Long -
el,___ gay and air - y,___ Yet__

dim.   *cresc.*   *p*   *cresc.* -

temps en - cor! Dou - ce flam -
one day more! Like a trea -

me,___ Je te gar - de___
sure___ I will guard___ thee,___

molto. -   -   -   *f*

dans mon â - me___ Com - me un tré -
naught my plea - sure___ E'er___ will re -

54

Un poco meno allegro, ma poco.

13203

Dou — ce flam — — me,
Like a trea — — sure

Res — — te dans mon â — — me
I fond - ly will guard thee,

Comme un
Naught will

doux tré - sor_____ Long — — temps en — —
thee re - store_____ When thou art

cor!_____ Ah!_____
o'er!_____ Ah!_____

Comme un tré - sor   Long - - - temps__ en - cor! ____
Naught will re - store   When _____ thou__ art o'er! ____

Nº 3 bis. Recit.

58

№ 4. Madrigal
à due.

13203

Juliet.

Pour pri - er   seu - le - ment!
They em - ploy   them in prayer!

u - ne bou - che ver - meil - le
and they sure - ly may use them!

Romeo.

N'en -
And

ten - dent - el - les pas   la voix, qui leur con - seil - le Un ar -
will   they nev - er hear   a voice that in - ly sues them, Or shall

Juliet.
poco animando.

rêt plus clé - ment?   Aux pri - è - res d'a - mour   leur
faith earn de - spair?   To all prayers born of love   their

p

cœur reste in - sen - si - ble, Même   en les e - xau - çant!
hearts will nev - er heark-en, Tho'   well they hear the   vow!

p

13203

Romeo.

E - xau - cez donc mes vœux___ et gar - dez im-pas - si - ble Vo -
Oh, hear my ar - dent vow!___ And tho' blush - es may dark-en, Still___

Tempo I. (*molto determinato*)

Juliet.

Ah!___ je n'ai pu m'en dé - fen - dre! J'ai pris
Ah!___ I've no pow'r to re - fuse it! Now my

- tre front rou-gis - sant!
___ un-mov'd be your brow!

Tempo I. (*molto determinato*)

Romeo.

le pé - ché pour moi!___ Pour a - pai - ser vo-tre é - moi!___ Vous plaît -
own the sin shall be!___ Mine let the sin ev - er be!___ Give it

Juliet. *cresc.* **Romeo.**

il de me le ren - dre? Non! je l'ai pris! lais - sez - le moi! Vous
me, and you will lose it! No! it is mine! Ah, leave it me! No!

Juliet.

Nº 5. Finale.

13203

Adagio. **Juliet.**(terrified).

'C'é - tait Ro - mé - o!
'Twas Ro - meo him - self!

(absorbedly, with fixed gaze)

Ah!___ je l'ai vu trop tôt___ sans le con -
Ah!___ Too ear-ly seen un-known, and known too

naî - tre!___ La haine est le ber-ceau de cet a-mour fa -
late!___ Fell ha - tred is the cra-dle of this fa - tal

tal!___ C'en est fait!___ si je ne puis être à
love!___ Woe is me!___ If I nev-er his may

lui,___ Que le cer-cueil soit mon lit nup-ti -
be,___ For me the grave, then a bride-bed shall

13203

68

Mercutio (to Romeo.)

l'ai — — me! Voy-ez! voy-ez de quel air fu-ri-
love ___ her! See there! see there! how with eye all a-

Tybalt.

Je tremble de
With fu-ry I'm

eux Ty-balt nous re-gar-de! Un o-rage est dans l'air...
flame We're fol-low'd by Ty-balt: There's a storm in the air.

Capulet.

ra — ge! Quoi! par-tez-vous dé-jà? de-meu-rez___ un ins-
shak — ing! What! will you leave so soon? Wait a while ere you

tant,___ de-meu-rez___ un ins-tant! Un sou-per joy-eux vous at-
go,___ wait a while___ ere you go! There is yet a banquet be-

tend!___ Un sou-per joy-eux vous at-tend!___
low,___ there is yet a banquet be-low!___

13203

72

13203

Je te dé - fends___ de faire un pas!___
And I for - bid you to take a step!___

Al - lons! jeunes gens! Al - lons! belles da - mes! Aux
A hall, mer-ry men! A hall, bonny ladies! Who

plus_di - li - gents Ces yeux pleins de___ flammes! Ces yeux, ces
will__ not__ be__ won Where beau - ty__ ar - ray'd is, Be won, where

yeux pleinsde__ flam - mes! Nar - gue! nar - gue des__ cen -
beau-ty__ ar - ray'd_____ is? Down them, down them, grum - blers

End of Act I.

Act II.

The Garden of Juliet.

Nº 6. Entr'acte and Chorus.

80

Allegretto. (♩=112.)

Chorus. (behind the scenes.)

TENORS.

Mys - té - ri - eux et som - bre, Ro - mé - o ne nous en - tend pas!
Wan-d'ring a - lone and sad - ly, To our call he will not re - ply!

BASSES.

Mys - té - ri - eux et som - bre, Ro - mé - o ne nous en - tend pas!
Wan-d'ring a - lone and sad - ly, To our call he will not re - ply!

Mys - té - ri - eux et som - bre, Ro - mé - o ne nous en - tend pas! L'a-mour se plaît dans
Wan-d'ring a - lone and sad - ly, To our call he will not re - ply! In shade love hid - eth

Mys - té - ri - eux et som - bre, Ro - mé - o ne nous en - tend pas! L'a-mour se plaît dans
Wan-d'ring a - lone and sad - ly, To our call he will not re - ply! In shade love hid - eth

l'om - bre, l'a-mour se plaît dans l'om - bre, Puis - se l'a - mour gui - der ses
glad - ly, in shade love hid - eth glad - ly, Well may he now on love re -

l'om - bre, l'a-mour se plaît dans l'om - bre, Puis - se l'a - mour gui - der ses
glad - ly, in shade love hid - eth glad - ly, Well may he now on love re -

13203

(Orch.)

№ 7. Cavatina.

Romeo.

L'a-mour! la-mour! oui,__ son ar - deur a troublé tout mon
On love! On love! Ay, for my heart in his bondage is

ê - tre!
aching!

Adagio. (♩=52.)

Mais quel - le sou - dai - ne clar - té re - splen-
But what sud - den light doth mine eye now be -

pp

dit à cet - te fe - nê - tre?
hold thro' yon win-dow breaking?

C'est là que dans la
The ray of morn-ing

L'istesso tempo. (♪=50.)

nuit ray - on - ne sa beau - té!
'tis, and Ju - liet is the sun!__

84

13203

№ 8. Scene and Choruses.

Romeo.

Non! je ne veux plus l'ê - tre Si ce nom dé - tes - té me sé - pa - re de
No! Nev-er will I own it, If a name so ab - horr'd shall di-vide thee from

toi! _ Pour t'ai - mer, lais - se - moi re - naî - tre, Lais-se - moi re -
me! _ Call me love! So _ may I a - tone it, so may I a -

cresc.

Allegro.

naî - tre Dans un au - tre que moi! _
tone it, For I love _ on - ly thee! _

Juliet. Recit. Moderato.

Ah! _ tu sais que la nuit te ca - che mon vi -
Ah! _ Thou know-est, the veil of night _ my face con -

Molto moderato.

sa - ge! Tu le sais! _ si tes yeux en voyaient la rou -
ceal - eth! Thou dost know! _ If thine eyes to per-ceive had the

13203

92

13203

93

13203

Chorus.

98

13203

100

13203

Gertrude.

Bé-ni soit le bâ-ton qui tôt ou tard me ven-ge De ces co-
Ev-er blest be the cud-gel that shall once be fall-ing Up-on your

Juliet.

C'est toi, Ger-tru-de?

Gertrude. I'st thou, dear Gertrude?

quins! Oui, mon bel an - ge! A cette heu - re com-
backs! Ay, pretty dar - ling! Tell me why, at this

3
Je t'at-tendais! Ne gronde
You were not here! Pray do not

ment ne re-posez-vous pas? Ren - trons!
hour, you are not in the fold? Come in!

p

(After glancing around, she reënters the pavillon, followed by Gertrude.) (Romeo reappears.)

pas!
scold!

pp

pp

№ 9. Duet.

104

Andante.

Moderato.

à - me! Si tu me veux pour fem-me, Fais-moi di - re quel jour, à quelle
ho - ly! Say, if thou love me tru-ly! Let me know on what day,— at what

heu-re, en quel lieu,— Sous le re-gard de Dieu notre u-ni - on se-ra bé-
hour, in what place We in the sight of God, in ho-ly bonds shall be u-

ni - e! A - lors, ô mon sei - gneur!____ sois mon u-ni-que
nit - ed. Then thou, my dear-est lord,____ my on-ly law shalt

loi;— Je te li - vre ma vie en - tiè - re, Je te li - vre ma vie en-
be!— Un-to thee all my life I ten - der, un-to thee all my life I

cresc.

tiè - re, Et je re - ni - e Tout,— ce qui n'est pas toi!
ten - der, All else be slighted, All,— that is not of thee!

f

p

13203

je te l'ai dit, je t'a-do - re! Dis - si - pe ma
I say a-gain, I a-dore thee! Dis-pel thou my

cresc.

nuit!__ sois l'au - ro - re, sois l'au-rore Où va mon
night!__ Send be-fore thee, Send be-fore thy rays, oh

cresc.

dim.

cœur, où vont mes yeux!_____ Dis - pose en
sun, re-joice mine eyes!_____ My heart can

dim.

rei - ne, dis - po - se de ma vi - e,
on - ly de - sire what-e'er thou will - est,

cresc.

Verse à mon âme i - nas-sou - vi - e, Verse__
Thou all my soul with rap-ture fill - est, thou__

cresc.

molto.

main! De cet a - dieu__ si douce est la tris - tes - se, Que
dawn! Of this fare - well__ so ten - der is the sor - row, That

je voudrais te dire a - dieu,__ que je voud-rais te dire a -
I were fain to say fare - well,__ that I were fain to say fare -

dieu jus - qu'à de - main! De cet a - dieu__ si
well un - til the dawn! Of this fare - well__ so

Dou - ce - ment   vien-ne se po - ser!_____
May the smile   for thy lov - er be,_____

Et mur-mur-ant en-cor:_____ Je t'aime! à ton o - reil - le   Que la
Murm'-ring a-gain,"I love thee!"A-gain nearthee in seem - ing!   May the

poco rit.   *a tempo.*

bri - se des nuits_____ te por-te ce bai - ser!_____
breez - es of night_____ bear on_my kiss to   thee!_____

(curtain.)

p   *pp*

End of Act II.

Act III.

The Cell of Friar Laurence.

№ 10. Entr'acte and Scene.
1st Tableau.

Allegro agitato. (♩= 96)

Romeo.

Moderato.

Mon
Good

pè - re! Dieu vous gar - de! Dieu vous gar - de!
mor-row, ho - ly Fa-ther! Fair good mor - row!

F. Laurence.
Recit.

Eh! quoi! le jour à pei-ne Se lè-ve, et le sommeil te
How now? The day but hard-ly is break-ing, And slum-ber flees thine

Recit.

fuit? Quel trans-port vers moi te con - duit?— Quel amoureux sou-ci t'a-
eye?— Why to me so ear-ly dost hie?— What cares of love com-pel thy

_p_ _cresc._ _dim._

Romeo.

Vous l'avez de - vi - né, mon pè - re, c'est l'a-
You di-vine it a - right, my Fa - ther; it is

mè - ne?
wak - ing?

_p_ _f_ _dim._

mour!— Quel nom prononcez-
love!— That name I have for-

L'amour! en - cor l'in - di - gne Ro - sa - li - ne.
'Tis love! A - gain th'un-wor-thy Ro - sa - line?—

p   *f*

Moderato e misurato.

vous? je ne le connais pas!— L'œil des é -
got, and with it all my woe!— When, borne on

f   *f*   *pp*

Ped.   ✻

lus,— s'ou - vrant à la clar-té di - vi - ne,
high,— the soul a-wakes in light di - vine,—

Ped.   ✻   Ped.   ✻   Ped.   ✻

Se souvient-il en - cor— des om-bres d'i-ci-
Can it re-mem - ber still— the gloom left here be-

Ped.   ✻   Ped.   ✻   Ped.   ✻

124

Voi-ci mon é - poux!__ Vous connais - sez ce cœur que je lui
be - hold__ my spouse!__ You know this heart that un - to him I

don - ne! À son amour je m'aban - don - ne; Devant le
prof - fer! Un - to his love my life I of - fer! In sight of

cresc.   f   dim.

F. Laurence.

ciel u - nis-sez - nous!__ Oui! dus - sé - je affron -
heav'n hal - low our vows!__ Ay! tho' blind be their

p   fp

Ped.

ter une a - veu - gle co - lè - re, Je vous prê - te - rai mon se -
ire when of - fense may be giv - en, I will lend my aid to you

fp   fp

13203

Nº 11. Trio and Quartet.

on:____ Re - gar - de d'un œil fa - vo - ra - ble Ta cré - a - tu - re mi - sé -
love!____ What - e'er their offense or transgres - sion, Look on them now in Thy com-

Juliet.

Sei - gneur! nous pro-met-
Oh Lord! Tru - ly we

ra - ble Qui se pros - ter - ne de-vant toi!__ Sei - gneur! nous pro-met-
pas - sion, Who bow be - fore Thine aw - ful throne!__ Oh Lord! Tru - ly we

Romeo.

tons d'o-bé - ir à ta loi.____ En - tends ma pri - è - re fer-
vow to o - bey Thee a - lone!____ May He, Who my pray'r yon - der

tons d'o-bé - ir à ta loi.____
vow to o - bey Thee a - lone!____

F. Laurence.

Ped. ✻

ven - - te! Fais que le joug de ta ser - van - - te Soit un
hear - - eth, Grant, that the yoke His handmaid bear - - eth, Be a

ben sostenuto.

joug   d'amour   et de   paix! ____   Que la ver-tu soit sa ri-
yoke   of love   un-al   loy'd! ____   Ev-er may vir-tue be her

che - se,   Que pour soute-nir sa fai-blesse Elle ar-me son cœur   du de-
dow - er;   Guid-ed and sustain'd by Thy pow'r May she in Thy fear   e'er a-

Juliet.

Sei - gneur, sois mon ap-pui, _ sois mon es-poir! _____
O   Lord! _ E'er be my   stay, _ e'er   be my   guide! _____

Romeo.

voir! _ Sei - gneur, sois mon ap-pui, _ sois mon es-poir! _____
bide! _ O   Lord! _ E'er be my   stay, _ e'er   be my   guide! _____

F. Laurence.

Que   leur vieillesse heu - reuse_ voie Leurs en-fants marchant dans ta
May   their old age be bless-ed, may Their chil-dren ev-er walk in Thy

134

13203

Public square before the palace of the Capulets.

Nᵒ 12. Chanson.
2ᵈ Tableau.

Poco animato.

mours!____ Aux vau - tours, il faut la ba - tail - le, Pour frap-
hest!____ For the vul - tures would fain be fight - ing, And their

p poco animato.

per d'e-stoc et de tail - le, Leurs becs sont ai - gui-
beaks are whet - ted for smit - ing; Full sharp are they, and

Tempo I.

sés!____ Lais - se là ces ois - eaux de proi - e, Tour - te-
strong!____ Fly a - way, then, from birds of prey, love! Thou wert

ten.

ten.

p

Ped.

rit.

rel - le qui fais ta joi - e Des a - mou - reux bai-
made on - ly to re - pay, love, Fond kiss - es warm and

rit pp

Ped.

Andantino. (♩ = 66)

sers! _____ Gar - dez bien la__ bel - le!
long! _____ Guard ye well her__ dwell - ing,

p

pp

138

tour de ce nid sau - va - ge A, je crois, sou - pi -
round yon-der ey - rie sigh - ing He did rove, so_they

poco animando

ré!_____ Les vau - tours sont à la cu - ré - e, Leurs chan -
say!_____ Lured a - field by a prey they're man - gling, Yet a -

sons que fuit Cy - thé - ré - e Ré - son - nent à grand
far the vul - tures are wran - gling, Their cries the ear af -

a tempo

bruit!_____ Ce - pen - dant, en leur douce i - vres - se Nos a -
fright!_____ And the while, fond - ly won in woo - ing, Lov - ers

mants con - tent leur ten - dres - se Aux as - tres de la
twain ten - der - ly_ are coo - ing 'Neath wond'ring stars of

attacca.

№ 13. Finale.

142

13203

ce pour nous nar - guer, mon jeu - ne ca - ma - ra - de, Que
will you here, young friend? Are you for quar-rel__ yearning, That

vous nous ré - ga - lez de cet-te__ sé - ré - na - de?
you re- gale us with your song at__ ear-ly__ morn - ing?

Stephano.

J'ai - me la mu - si - que!
I am fond of mu - sic!

C'est clair, c'est clair, On_ t'au -
'Tis clear, 'tis clear, Your gui -

ra sur_ le__ dos, en pa-reille é -qui - pé - e, Cas-sé ta gui - ta - re, mon cher!
tar, for_ a__ like sil- ly prank, was__ bro-ken, And o - ver your shoulders, my dear!

Chorus.

TENORS.

É - cou-tons, é - cou - tons   leur   chan - son.
Let us hear, let us   hear   how   they   sing.

BASSES.

É - cou-tons, é - cou - tons   leur   chan - son.
Let us hear, let us   hear   how   they   sing.

Quel - le ra - ge!   Ver - tu - dieu!   Bon cou - ra - ge!
What a fu - ry!   What a fray!   Ev - er war - y,

Quel - le ra - ge!   Ver - tu - dieu!   Bon cou - ra - ge!
What a fu - ry!   What a fray!   Ev - er war - y,

Bon cou-rage Et franc jeu! Voyez comme cet en - fant_____
Ev - er gay How they play! See how yonder pu - ny boy_____

Bon cou-rage Et franc jeu! Voyez comme cet en - fant_____
Ev - er gay How they play! See how yonder pu - ny boy_____

148

(Enter Tybalt, who answers the insult.)

di - gne des Ca - pu - lets!   Tels mai - tres,   tels va -
harms a Cap - u - let's name!   Like mas - ter,   like —

Tybalt (insolently.)

lets!   Vous a - vez la pa - ro - le prompt - te, mon - sieur!
man!   With your tongue you are ver - y read - y, I vow!

Mercutio.   **Tybalt.**

Moins prompt - te que le   bras!..   C'est ce qu'il fau - drait
My arm — is read - ier   still!   Sore - ly you'll need it

Mercutio.   (Mercutio and Tybalt engage;

voir!...   C'est ce que tu ver - ras!
now!   Try me when - e'er you will!

at the same instant, Romeo rushes in and tries to separate them.)

13203

150

(to Romeo, haughtily.)

Al - lons! vil Mon - tai - gu! flam-berge au
How now, thou wretched boy! Hast thou an

senza accelerare

vent! _____ dé - gaî - ne! Toi qui nous in - sul -
arm, _____ de - fend thee! Thou, who dost e - ven

tas _____ jus - quen no - tre mai -
dare _____ mock us all in our

son, C'est toi qui vas por - ter la
home, 'Tis now thou sore - ly shalt re -

pei - ne! De cette in - di - gne tra - hi - son!
pent thee That ev - er thith - er thou hast come!

colla voce

13203

Toi dont la bou-che mau - di - te À Ju-li-ette in-ter-di - te O-
Thy curs-ed lip e - ven near-ing Sli - ly to Ju - li-et's hear - ing, Where

a tempo (disdainfully.)

sa, je crois,— par-ler tout bas, É - cou - te le seul mot que m'ins-
it were best — for ev - er dumb! Now hear the on - ly name that my

colla voce   *a tempo*

cresc.

pi - re ma hai - ne!   Tu n'es qu'un lâ - che!
hate can pre - sent thee!   Thou art a vil - lain!

(Romeo seizes and half-draws

molto   *f*   *ff*   *pausa lungissima.*

his sword; after a moment's hesitation, he returns it to the scabbard.)

Andante. (♩ = 54.)

Romeo (contained and dignified.)

Al - lons! _____   tu ne me con-nais pas,   Ty - balt,
Not so! _____   Ty - balt, thou know'st me not!

152

13203

154

13203

(Tybalt and Mercutio engage.)

Mercutio.

Romeo.

Ah! bles-sé!   Bles-sé!
Ah! I'm hurt!   A hurt?

secco.

Un poco meno allegro, ma poco, sempre alla battuta ₵.

Mercutio.

Un poco meno allegro

Que le dia - ble
A plague

soit de vos deux mai - sons! Pour-quoi te je - ter en - tre
fall on your hous - es both! Why came you between us at

Romeo.

nous? Ô sort im-pi-toy-a-ble! se-cou-rez-
all? Oh Fate, bar-ren of pit-y! Aid him a-

Mercutio.

(Mercutio is borne away dying.)

le! Sou-te-nez moi!
way! Lend me a hand!

(Romeo, after following him with his eyes for a brief space, comes forward again, filled

molto.

with furious resentment, cries out:)

Romeo.

Ah! main-te-
Ah! he is

nant re-monte au ciel _____ pru-dence in-fâ-
slain! A-way to heav'n, _____ oh shame-ful cau-

me! / tion! Et toi, / And thou, fu - reur / oh fire - à l'œil / ey'd ret de flam - / ri - bu - me, / tion,

Sois de mon cœur / Now of my heart l'u - ni - que loi! / the law shalt be! Ty - balt! / Ty - balt!

Il n'est i - ci / None oth - er here d'au - tre / is a lâ - che que / vil - lain, but

(they engage.)

toi! / thee!

ff

Péd. ✳

ff

Péd. ✳ Péd. ✳

Romeo.

tant! Ah! qu'ai - je fait? moi! fuir, mau - dit par
may! What have I done? Ah! She ev - er will

cresc. -

Benvolio. **Romeo.**

el - - le! C'est la mort qui t'at - tend! Qu'el - le vien - ne
hate me! It is death if thou stay! Dir - er far than

Adagio. Tybalt. (to Capulet, with a final effort).

donc,— je l'ap - pel - - le! Un dernier mot! et sur votre
death may a - wait me! On - ly a word, and on your

f *f* *pp*

à - me ex - au - cez - moi!
hon - or swear to com - ply!

cresc. - - - *molto* -

Capulet. (solemnly).

Tu se - ras o - bé - is, je t'en don - ne ma
On my hon - or, I swear! Do on me thou re -

dim. *p*

168

13203

13203

J'ai ven-gé mon a - mi,_____ que mon sort s'ac-com - plis - se!
I a-veng-ed my friend:_____ with my life I will an - swer!

Stephano. Andante. *ff*
Jus - ti - - ce! Jus - ti - - ce!
A - venge__ us! A - venge__ us!

Romeo.
Jus - ti - - ce! Jus - ti - - ce!
A - venge__ us! A - venge__ us!

Benvolio.
Jus - ti - - ce! Jus - ti - - ce!
A - venge__ us! A - venge__ us!

Paris, Gregorio, Capulet.
Jus - ti - - ce!
A - venge__ us!

TENORS. The Montagues. Andante. *ff*
Jus - ti - - ce! Jus - ti - - ce!
A - venge__ us! A - venge__ us!

BASSES. The Capulets.
Jus - ti - - ce!
A - venge__ us!

Andante.

Lento. The Prince.
Eh quoi? tou-jours du sang! de vos cœurs in-humains
What now? For ev - er blood? Of your hearts, bent on harm,

13203

172

18203

Mon cœur se brise é - per - du de dou - leur!
Break - ing, my heart fails in pain and de - spair!

dim.

In - juste ar - rêt qui trop tard nous dé - sar - mes,
Tho' we dis - arm, how un - time - ly the warn - ing!

p
cresc.

Tu mets le comble à ce jour de mal - heur!
For we may nev - er thy rav - age re - pair!

p

Je vois pé - rir dans le sang et les lar - mes
Ev - 'ry de - sire, ev - 'ry hope grim - ly scorn - ing,

p
cresc.
f

poco rit.

Tous les es - poirs et tous les vœux de mon
Weep - ing and blood a - lone in thee may we

poco rit.

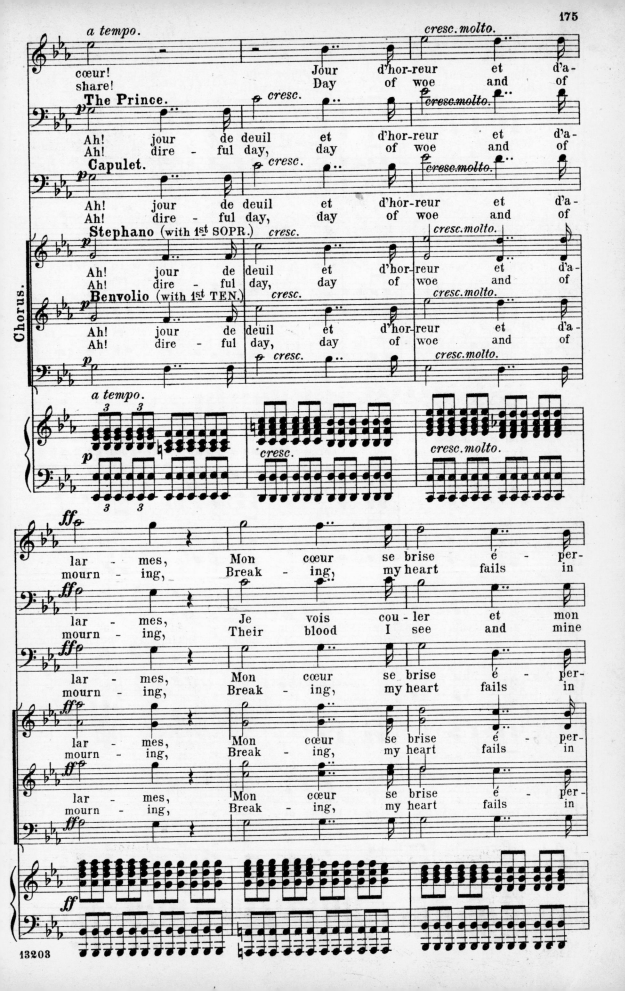

Andante maestoso.

End of Act III.

Nᵒ 14. The Chamber of Juliet.
1ˢᵗ Tableau.
(It is still night.)
Duet.

Juliet.

Romeo.

Piano.

Andantino.

Andantino. (♩ = 66).

cresc. molto.

Ped.

dim.

Ped.

Juliet.   Recit.

Va!___   je t'ai par-don - né,   Ty-balt   vou - lait ta
Love!___   Thy life   Ty-balt sought, and I   par - don thy

184

13203

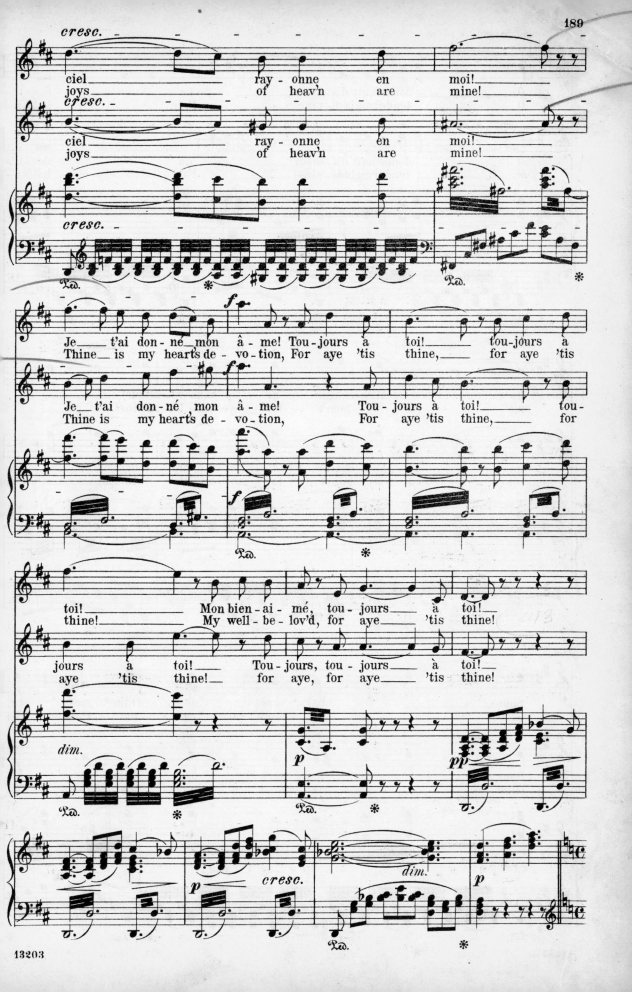

(Romeo listens, as to sounds without, and seems preoccupied.)

du bel as-tre des nuits! _____ Res-te! res-te!
from the dim-beam-ing moon! _____ Tar-ry! Tar-ry!

Romeo. Allegro. *ff* Recit.

Ah! vien-ne donc la
Ah! Be thou wel-come,

Andante molto appassioato.

mort! _____ je res-te!
Death! _____ I tar-ry!

(con delirio.) *ff*

(During this entire ritournelle, Juliet and Romeo remain entwined in each other's arms.)

cresc. molto.

194

Pars!— ma vi - e! Loi— cru -
Go,— be - lov-ed! Law— de -

Romeo.

Un bai - ser, et je pars!—
Yet a kiss, and I go!—

cresc.

p

ritard. ma pochiss.
Romeo.

el - le! loi—— cru - el - le! Ah! res - te!
spite - ful! Law— de - spite - ful! Ah! stay, love!

ritard. ma pochiss.

reste en - cor en mes bras en - la - cés!— Reste en -
Yet re - main so en - twin'd in my arms!— Yet re -

dim.

p

rit. *a tempo.*

cor!— reste en - cor! un jour il se - ra doux à
main!— Yet re - main! In faith - ful love se - cure, one

rit. *a tempo.*

p

Ped. *

notre a - mour fi - dè - le De se res - sou - ve - nir de ses tour-ments pas-
day 'twill be de - light-ful When we re - call to mem - o - ry our past a -

ritard.

pp *colla voce.*

pres - se! Et t'ar-ra-cher à cette ar-dente i - vres - se!
fold thee, Nor yet thy heart o-bey, that fain would hold thee!

pres - se! Et l'ar-ra-cher à cette ar-dente i - vres - se!
fold me, Nor yet my heart o-bey, that fain would hold me!

Ah! que le sort___ qui de toi___ me sé-pa- re,
Ah, fa-tal hour,___ that from thee___ me di-vid- eth,

Ah! que le sort qui de toi me sé-pa- re,
Ah, fa-tal hour, that from thee me di-vid- eth,

Plus que la mort___ est cru-el___ et bar-ba- re!
Thy cru-el pow'r___ more than death___ e'en be-tid- eth!

Plus que la mort est cru-el et bar-ba- re!
Thy cru-el pow'r more than death e'en be-tid- eth!

Il faut par-tir, hé-las! Il faut quit-ter ces bras___ Où je te
Thou must in-deed a-way, Nor in these arms de-lay___ Where I en-

Il faut par-tir, hé-las! A-lors que dans ses bras___ El-le me
I must in-deed a-way, Nor in these arms de-lay___ That now en-

(Juliet stands gazing fixedly at the balcony, over which Romeo has hastily departed.)

Andante. (♩ = 60) **Juliet.**

A - dieu! mon â - me!   a - dieu ma vi - e!
Fare-well, be - lov - ed!   May For-tune guide him!

(fervently.)

An - ges du ciel!   à vous,___ à vous je le con -
An - gels of heav'n,   to ye,___ to ye do I con -

fi - e!
fide___ him!

Nº 15. Quartet.

201

pro - té - ge - nous!
Thy will be done!

Allegretto. (♩ = 100)

Capulet. Recit.

Quoi! ma fil - le, la nuit à peine est a - che-
How, my daughter! The night her leave is hard-ly

vé - e, Et tes yeux sont ou - verts, et te voi - là le - vé - e!
tak-ing, And I find thee a - rous'd? 'Tis ear - ly for thy wak-ing!

13203

Hé - las!__ no-tre souci, je le vois, est pa reil,__
A - las!__ Our lov-ing cares, as I see are the same,

Et les mê-mes re - grets__ hâ - tent no-tre ré - veil!
And our wak-en-ing thoughts own a like wo-ful aim!

Andantino. (♩ = 72)

Que l'hym - ne nup - ti - al__ suc - cède aux cris d'a-
A wed - ding song shall soon__ o'er - bear the wail of

larmes! Fi - dèle au der-nier vœu___ que Ty - balt___ à for-
sor-row! To Ty - balt's dy - ing will___ let thy heart___ be in-

mé,___ Re - çois de lui l'époux que sa bouche à nom-
clin'd;___ From him re - ceive the spouse, whom for thee he de -

mé,___ Sou - ris___ au mi - lieu de tes lar -
sign'd, And smile___ 'mid thy tears on the mor -

Juliet.

mes! Cet é - poux___ quel est - il?___
row! And the spouse who is he?___

Juliet.

Dieu!
Ah!
F. Laur.

Le plus vaillant de tous,___ Le comte Pâ - ris! Si -
The bravest of them all___ the coun-ty Pa - ris! Be

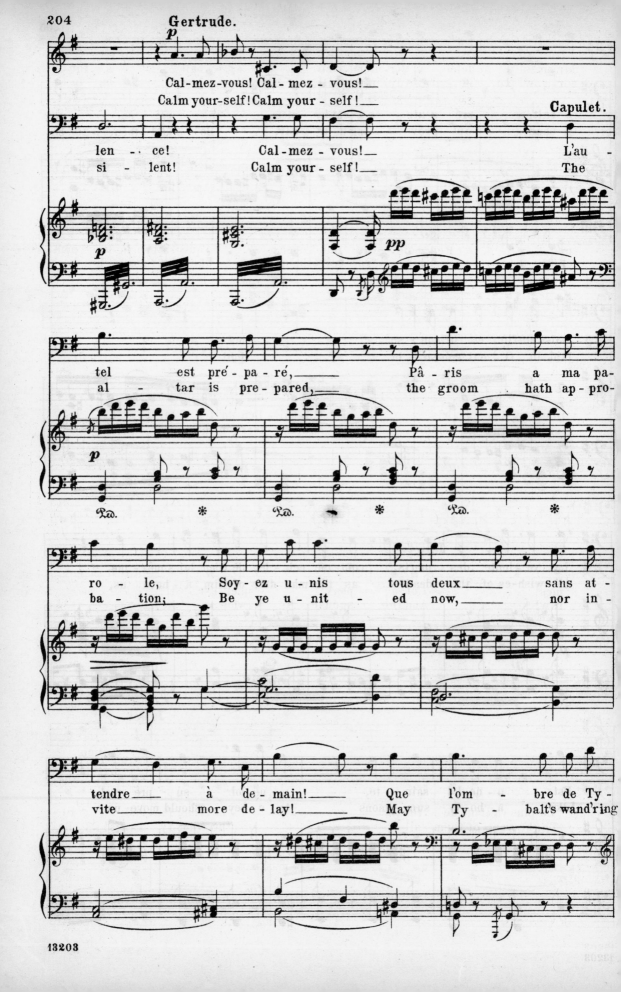

balt,___ pré - sente à cet hy - men,___ S'a - pai - se, s'a-

shade,___ ap - prov - ing us to - day,___ Be laid then, be

paise en-fin et te con - so - - - le.

laid in fi - nal con-so - la - - - tion!

La vo - lonté des morts,___ com - me cel - le de Dieu lui - mê - me,

All wish-es of the dead,___ as the man-date of Him a - bove us,

Est u - ne loi sain - te, u - ne loi su - prê - me!

Like a ho-ly sum - mons to o - bey should move us:

cœur est sans re-mords, mon cœur est sans re - mords!

heart is faithful still, my heart is faithful still!

laissons en paix dor - mir les morts!

well may they sleep nor, dream of ill!

la vo-lon - té des morts!

let us re - gard, their will!

mon cœur par - ta - ge ses re - mords!

heart sad fore - bod - ings now do fill!

p

Capulet.

Frè - re Lau - rent sau-ra te dic-ter ton de - voir.

You, ho-ly Fa - ther, can in - struct her du - ty, I trow:

p

Nos a - mis vont ve - nir je vais les re - ce - voir.

But our friends will ar - rive; I go to meet them now.

f

f *dim.* *p* *cresc.*

Nº 16. Scene.

et mon a-mour cou-pa-ble; C'est à vous de me se-cou-
Nor did my love dis-cov-er; 'Tis on you I a-lone re-

rir,— à vous de m'ar-ra-cher à mon sort mi-sé-ra-ble! Par-
ly,— To you on-ly I look to re-store me my lov-er! Oh

lez, mon pè-re, Par-lez!— ou bien je suis prête à mou-
speak, my Father! Oh speak!— Or tor-tur'd by an-guish I

Andante. F. Laurence. Recit. Juliet.

rir! Ain-si, la mort— ne trouble point votre â-me? Non!
die! And so,— for you,— Death has no more of ter-ror? No!

Recit.

Moderato.

non! plu-tôt la mort— que ce mensonge in-fâ-me!
no! Far bet-ter die,— than live in shameful er-ror!

13203

Andante. (♩=63.)
F. Laurence.

Bu - vez donc ce breu - va - - - - ge:
What this phi-al en - clos - - - - es,

Et des membres au cœur _____ Va sou-dain se ré-
If you drink, then a chill _____ From the limbs to the

pandre u -ne froi - de lan - gueur, _____ De la mort men-son-gère i -
heart all your frame shall o'er - thrill, _____ That as dead your warm life re-

ma - - - ge. Dans vos vei - nes sou-dain le sang s'arrê-te-
pos - - - es; In your veins, _____ at once, the blood, ceasing to

F. Laurence.

C'est là qu'après un jour vo - tre corps et votre â - me, Com-
And there, with-in a day, shall your heart feel a striv - ing, As

me d'un foyer mort se ra - ni - me la flam - me, Sor-ti - ront en-
when on chil-ly hearth for-mer flame is re - viv - ing, And your heav-y

fin de ce lourd som-meil; Par l'ombre pro-té - gés, votre é-
sleep you shall then for-sake! O'er-shadow'd by the night, with your

poux et moi-mê - me Nous é - pi - rons, nous é - pi - rons vo - tre ré-
spouse I'll e - spy you; We shall be nigh, we shall be nigh when you a-

veil ___ Et vous fui - rez au bras de ce - lui qui vous ai - me,
wake, ___ And you shall flee a - way with him whom they de - ny you,

Et vous fui - rez au bras de ce - lui qui vous ai -
and you shall flee a - way with him whom they de - ny

me!
you!

Hé - si - tez - vous? Non!
Do you re - pent? No!

Juliet.

Moderato. *L'istesso movimento.*

non! à vo - tre main j'ab - ban - don - ne ma vi - e!
no! I will con - fide e - ven life to your keep - ing!

F. Laurence. **Juliet.** (firmly.) (Exit F. Laurence.)

À de - main! À de - main!
For a day! For a day!

Ballet.

Nº 17. Scene and Air.*⁾

Si ce breu-vage é-tait sans pou-voir!___
What if this po-tion work not at all?___

(with confidence.) **Moderato.** (resolutely.)

cresc.

Craintes vai-nes! Je n'appartiendrai pas au
I - dle ter-rors! They can-not make me wed the

f

Comte mal-gré moi! Non! non! ce poi - gnard,___ ce poi-
county 'gainst my will! No! no! For this poignard, this___

f *f* *f* *f* *f*

gnard se - ra le gar-dien___ de ma foi! Viens!___
poi-gnard shall be the guard___ of my vow! Come!___

f

___ viens!___
___ Come!___

Moderato ben risoluto. (♩ = 84)

A - mour＿ ra - ni＿ me mon cou -
O love,＿ re-vive my fond de -

ra - - ge, Et de mon cœur chas - - se＿ l'ef -
vo - - tion, And from my heart ban - -ish＿ dis -

froi!＿ Hé - si - ter, c'est＿ te faire ou -
may!＿ Now to doubt, that＿ were to＿ dis -

tra - - ge, Trem - bler,＿ est un manque de
own thee, To fear,＿ were my love to be -

foi! Ver - - se! ver - - se!
tray! Nev - - er! Nev - - er!

220

13203

Tempo I.

l'om-bre des tourments pas - sés! Viens!_____ A -
bove the gloom of woes gone by! Come!_____ Oh

dim.   p f   dim.

mour!_____ ra - ni - me mon cou - ra - - ge Et de mon
love!_____ revive my fond de - vo - tion, And from my

p

cœur chas - - se l'ef - froi!_____ Hé - si -
heart ban - - ish_ dis - may;_____ Now to

ter, c'est____ te faire ou - tra - - ge! Trem -
doubt, that____ were to dis - own thee! To

cresc.

bler,_____ est un man-que de foi! Ver -
fear,_____ were my love to be - tray! Nev -

f   p ff   p

va - ge! O Ro-mé - o,___ je bois à toi!___
moan me! O my be - lov'd,___ I will o - bey!___

je bois à toi!___
I will o - bey!___

colla voce.

End of Act IV.
(in ordinary stage-performance.)

№ 18. Nuptial Procession.

Allegro maestoso. ($\bullet$ = 112.)

(Wind-instr.s on stage.)

Piano.

[1] (Continue with the Finale, on p. 238.)

228

Nº 18. Epithalamium.*)

*) This number is omitted in performance.

13203

230

13203

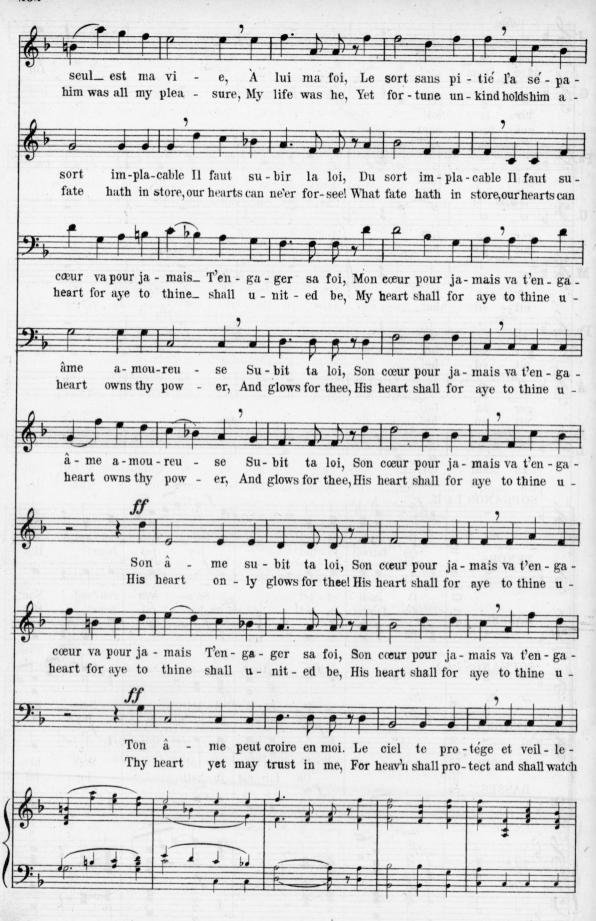

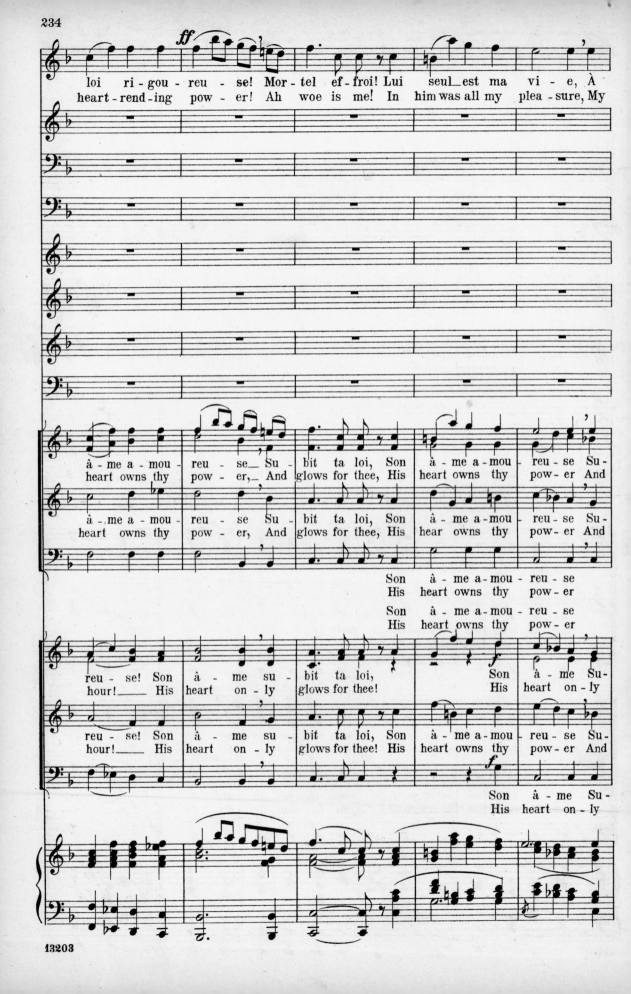

loi ri-gou-reu-se! Mor-tel ef-froi! Lui seul est ma vi - e, À
heart-rend-ing pow-er! Ah woe is me! In him was all my plea-sure, My

à - me a-mou - reu - se Su - bit ta loi, Son à - me a-mou - reu - se Su-
heart owns thy pow - er, And glows for thee, His heart owns thy pow- er And

à - me a-mou - reu - se Su - bit ta loi, Son à - me a-mou - reu - se Su-
heart owns thy pow - er, And glows for thee, His hear owns thy pow- er And

Son à - me a-mou - reu - se
His heart owns thy pow - er

Son à - me a-mou - reu - se
His heart owns thy pow - er

reu - se! Son à - me su - bit ta loi, Son à - me Su-
hour!___ His heart on - ly glows for thee! His heart on - ly

reu - se! Son à - me su - bit ta loi, Son à - me a-mou - reu - se Su-
hour!___ His heart on - ly glows for thee! His heart owns thy pow- er And

Son à - me Su-
His heart on - ly

235

236

13203

Nº 19. Finale.

240

End of Act IV.

Act V.

№ 20. Entr'acte.

№ 20bis. Scene.

par - te cet - te nuit mê — me! Ve-nez! chaque in-stant de re-
Bear him the fa - tal let - ter! A-way! 'tis a per-il-ous

Allegro moderato.

tard __ Nous jette en un pé - ril ex - trê - me!
plight! __ The soon - er he is gone, the bet - ter!

dim.

Adagio.

pp

Ped. *

The Tomb.

Nº 21. Juliet's Slumber.

№ 22. Scene and Duet.

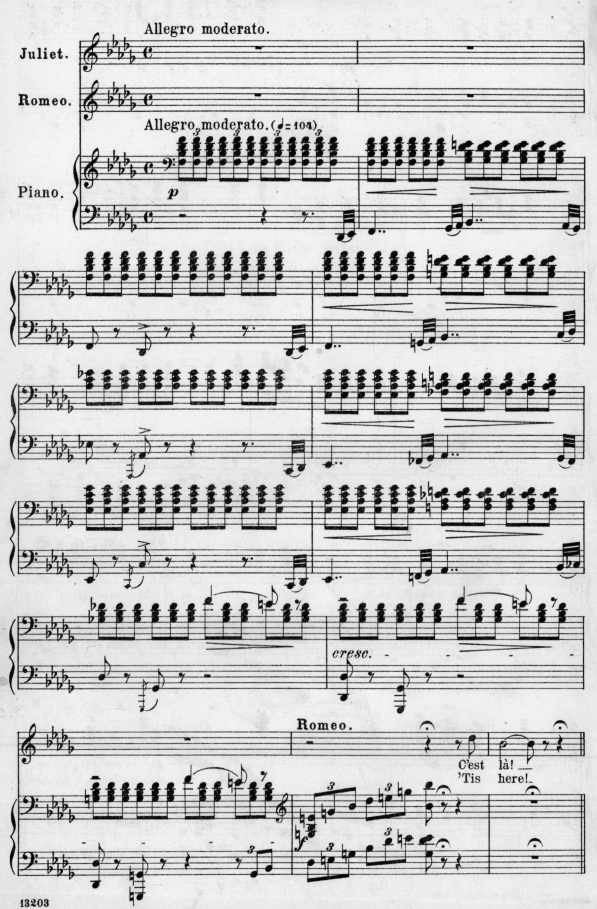

Andante.   (with an expression of awe.)

Sa - lut! __ tom-
Oh tomb! __ Thy

beau! sombre et si - len - ci - eux! __ Un tom-
frown dark - ly my gaze de - fies! __ A

a tempo

beau! non non! __ ô de-meu-re plus bel - le
tomb! No, no! __ Oh yet love-lier a dwel - ling

Que le sé-jour mê - me des cieux! _____ Sa - lut, __ pa - lais_ splen-
Than yon fair a - bode in the skies! _____ How bright thy front! A

Recit.

dide et ra-di - eux! _ Ah! la voi - là! c'est el -
pal - ace it out - vies! _ Ah, she is there, my dar-

250

13203

co - re,   Et sou - rire_ à l'é - ter - ni - té!!!_
per - ish,   Like a   smile_ on e - ter - ni - ty!_

Pourquoi me la rends-tu si belle,   ô mort li -
Why give her me a - gain so love-ly, thou pale de -

vi - de?...   Est-ce pour me je - ter plus vi - te dans ses   bras?__
stroy-er?   Is it   to draw me ear-lier yet_ to her em - brace?__

(portamento.)

Va! c'est le seul bon-heur dont mon cœur soit a - vi - de!...   Et ta proie aujourd'-
Ah! it   is on - ly thus that my heart can en - joy her!   And thy prey shall to-

Andante. (♩ = 66.)

hui   ne t'é - chap-pe - ra   pas.__
night here meet thee face to   face!__

Ah!_ je te con-tem-ple sans crainte, Tombe où je vais en-fin _ près
Ah!_ Less have I dread-ed thee nev-er, Tomb where I shall at last_ re-

cresc.

p

d'el - le re - po - ser!_ Ô mes bras,_ don-nez-
pose, no more to grieve; Oh my arms!_ This em-

dim. *p* *p cresc.*

lui vo - tre dernière é - trein-te! Mes lè-vres, don-nez-lui vo-tre der-
brace shall be your last for ev - er! My lips,_ take ye now a long fare-

molto *f*

Andante. (he embraces Juliet deliriously.)

nier _ bai - ser!... well _ to love!

ff

Ped. * Ped. * Ped. * Ped. *

ff (with frenzy.) (He empties the vial at one

À toi, ma Ju-li - et - te!
To thee, O, my be-lov - ed!

ff

Ped. * Ped. *

draught, and casts it on the ground; then reels, and sinks gradually on the steps of the monument. At

this moment, Juliet begins to shake off her lethargy; she rises slowly, and gazes about her with a be-

wildered air.) **Juliet.**   **Romeo.** (listening.)

Où   suis -   je?   Ô ver-
Where am   I?   Oh a-

ti - ge!   Est-ce un rê - ve?
maze - ment!   Am I   dream - ing?

Sa bouche a mur- mu-ré   mes doigts en fré-mis-
'Twas sure-ly she who spoke!   My hands, touch-ing her

13203

254

sant Ont sen-ti dans les siens la cha-leur de son sang!_____ El-le me re-
own, All a-trem-ble have felt that her blood yet is warm!_____ Now on me she

(He gazes on Juliet
fixedly and in amazement.)

gar-de_____ et se lè - ve!!!
gaz-es_____ she a - ris - es!

Adagio. **Juliet.** (gently.) **Romeo.** (with an outburst)

Ro-mé-o!_____ Sei-gneur Dieu tout puis-sant! El - le
Ro - meo!_____ Oh, Al-might-y on high! She's a-

vit! El-le vit!_____ Ju-li-ette est vi-van-te!
live! She's a-live!_____ My__ Ju-liet is liv-ing!

Moderato. **Juliet.**

Dieu! quelle est cet-te
Ah! what voice do I

13203

255

13203

262

miè - - re,   Se   perd _____ dans l'infi-
mor - - tal   The   soul _____ hie - eth to

Più animato. (♩=88.) **Juliet.**

- ni.   Ô   dou - leur!! _   ô   tor - tu - re!!!
day!   Oh   de - spair! _   Oh, what an - guish!

Moderato. (♩=80.) **Romeo.**

É - coute, ô Ju - li - et - te!   L'a - lor - et - te dé -
But hark, Ju - liet, my dar - ling!   'Tis the lark yon - der

Andante.

jà nous an - non - ce le jour!!! _   Non! _ non, ce n'est pas le
calls, to re - mind us of day! _   No, _ no! it is not the

jour, _____   ce n'est pas   l'a - lou - et - te!
day, _____   nor the lark's ear - ly call - ing!

13203

End of Opera.